TIME ZONE   SÄTTY

TIME ZONE

SÄTTY

Straight Arrow Books

Library of Congress
Catalog Card Number:
73-79877

ISBN: 0-87932-028-1
(clothbound)
0-87932-067-2
(paperbound)

Order numbers:
102028 (cloth)
102067 (paper)

First Printing

Straight Arrow Books
625 Third Street
San Francisco, CA 94107

Distributed by
Quick Fox Inc
33 West 60 Street
New York, NY 10023

Production by
Planned Production

Printed in the United
States of America by
California Printing Com-
pany, San Francisco

Typeset in Optima by
Mercury Printing Co,
San Francisco

Published in association with Robert Briggs

Also by Sätty:
The Cosmic Bicycle

PRÈFAÇE

There is a time in the span of civilizations when creative energy and the human spirit are wholly, if briefly focussed. When this occurs culture in all its manifestations reaches its zenith. The moment passes; civilizations decline, only to be replaced by others. This process of life appears cyclic. Communities become tribes, turn into nations and become empires which, like suns, radiate their energy to the limits of their power, then decay and finally vanish, leaving behind only traces. This cycle, which may continue until our sun—or our planet—fails us, is the principal concern of my book.

Time Zone tells a story using printed images derived from past and present. This visual vocabulary is more universal and intelligible than a verbal language and can be experienced on many levels. A tale told in such a language is timely since we live in an age when visual forms are the dominant vehicle of communication through the pervasive use of electronic and printed media. An enormous barrage of images has been indiscriminately disseminated, presenting a confusing vision of the world that forces even innocent children into a neurotic life experience.

The experience of receiving all this bewildering information creates an unhealthy emotional environment which, like the physical environments man creates, appears subject to the balancing process of nature. Since Man is a part of nature, he must continually re-examine his role in relation to the natural experience.

We are at a critical turn: for the artificial emotional environment we have created is not in balance, has not been defined, nor has the extent of its influence been determined. If this condition continues we may unconsciously be triggering a form of mass insanity and premature decay, signs of which are already visible. Understanding this may help us clarify our reality so we can find a way to complete a natural cycle.

Towards this understanding—a new beginning—this book is dedicated.

San Francisco
Spring, 1973

INTRŌDUCTION

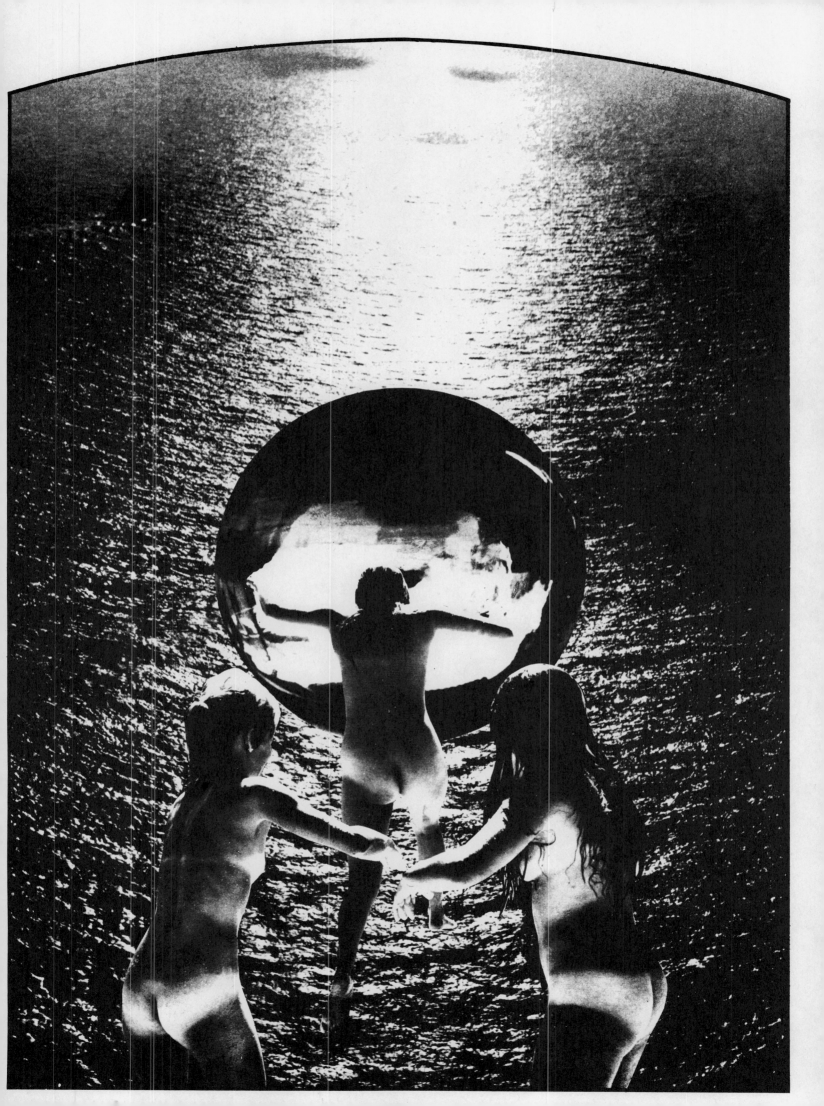

THE LAND

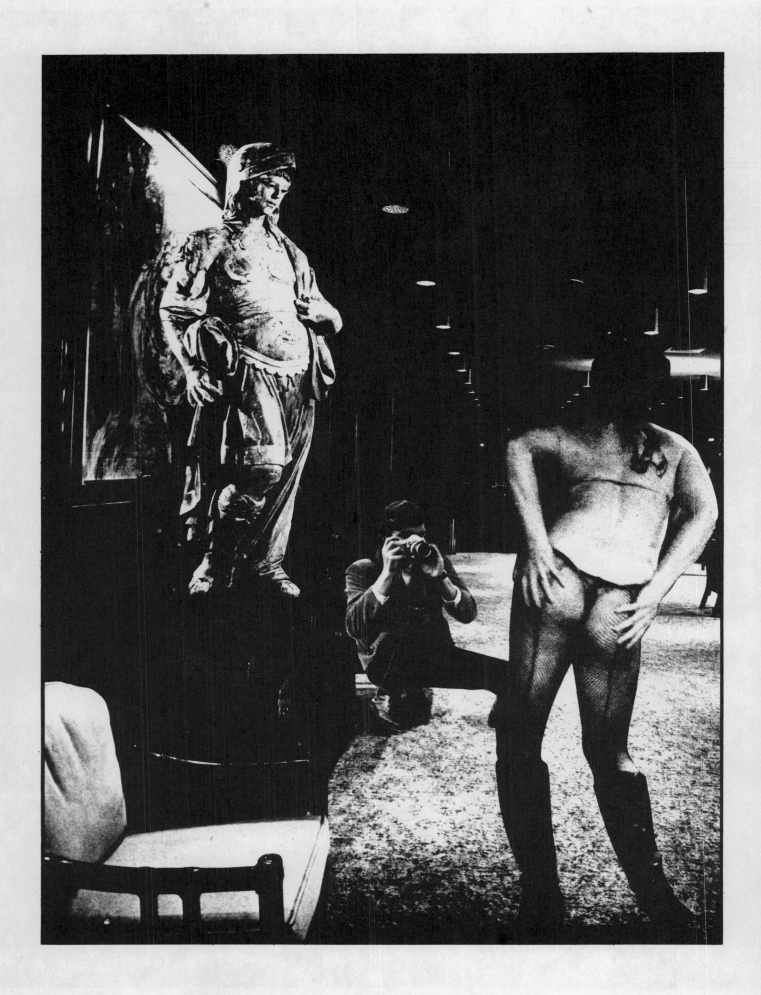

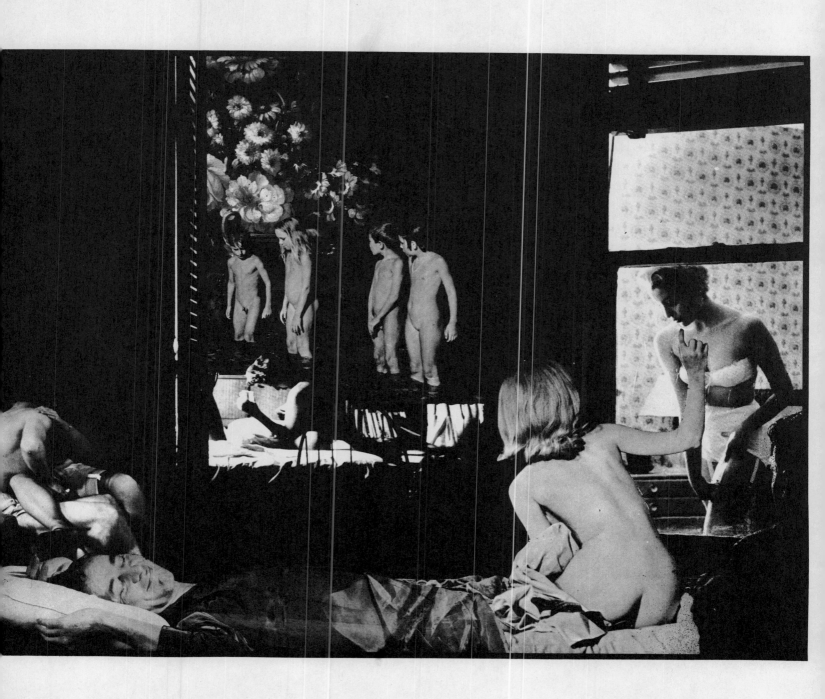

ANOTHER TIME

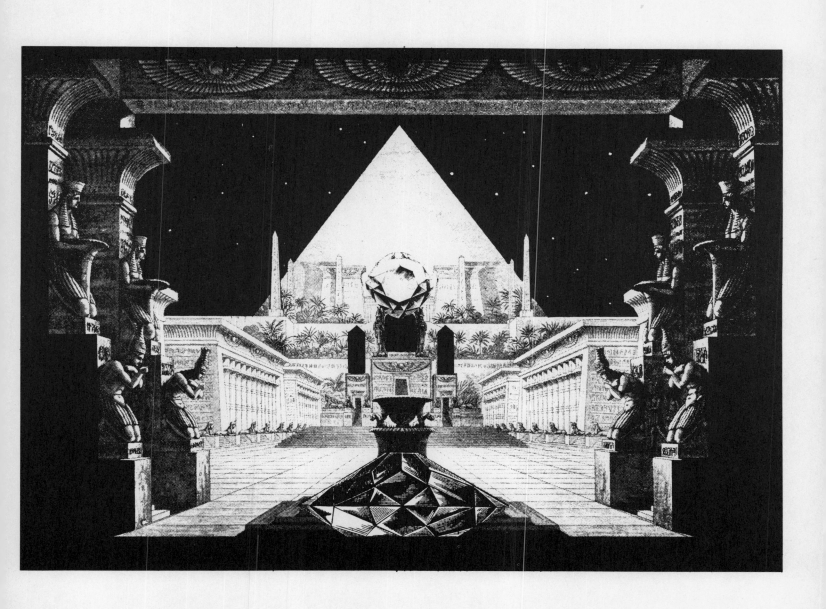

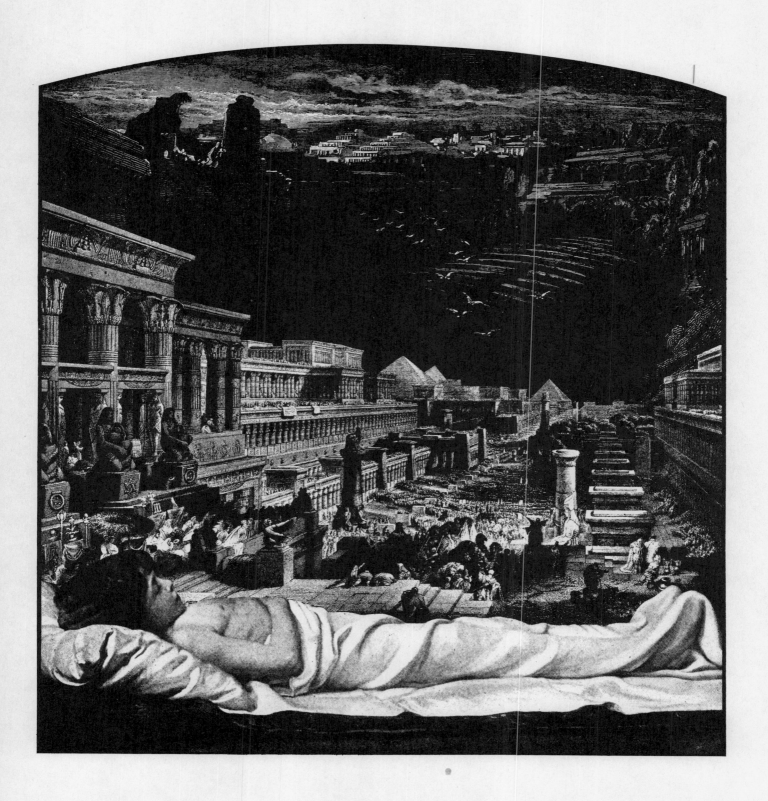

99

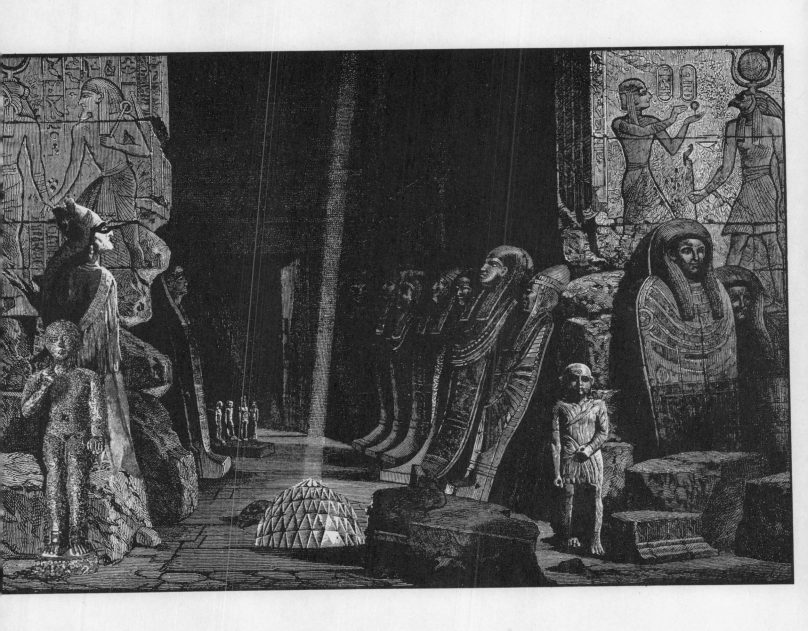

HYMN OF DELIVERANCE

113

A VANISHED CIVILISATION

The author gratefully acknowledges the following for their inspiration and contribution which helped make this book possible: David Singer, Walter Medeiros, Alain de Boisanger, John Grissim, Martha McKay, Mary Wagner, Nick Nichols, Jon Goodchild, Alan Rinzler, Don Birkenseer, Robert Hawley, David Charlsen.

Straight Arrow Books: Dian Aziza Ooka, Mick Stevens, Darlene Gremli, Rosemary Nightingale, Linda Gunnarson, Barbara Bur-gower, Douglas Mount.